Biff's spade was no good.

Dad got a big spade.

"Let me dig a hole," he said.

Dad dug a hole.

The children helped.

The hole got bigger…

…and bigger,

...and deeper

...and deeper.

All the children came.

They played in the hole.

The water came in.

"I can't stop it," said Dad.

The tide came in.

Dad's spade was in the hole.

Next day, the hole had gone.

Dad's spade was under the sand.

"Let's dig," said Dad.